Big Workbook
Phonics

Bath · New York · Cologne · Melbourne · Delhi
Hong Kong · Shenzhen · Singapore

Helping your child

- Remember that the activities in this book should be enjoyed by your child. Try to find a quiet place to work.

- Always give your child lots of encouragement and praise.

- Remember that the gold stars are a reward for effort as well as for achievement.

- Your child does not need to complete each page in one go. Always stop before your child grows tired, and come back to the same page another time.

- It is important to work through the pages in the right order because the activities do get progressively more difficult.

- The answers to the activities are on pages 124–128.

This edition published by Parragon Books Ltd in 2017

Parragon Books Ltd
Chartist House
15-17 Trim Street
Bath BA1 1HA, UK
www.parragon.com

Copyright © Parragon Books Ltd 2017

Written by Nina Filipek
Illustrated by Simon Abbott
Educational Consultant: Janet Rose

ISBN 978-1-4748-7581-3

Printed in China

Selected contents

A snake goes **hissssss**

A bee goes **buzzzzzzz**

What sounds do these animals make?
Make your own sound effects for each picture below.

Note for parent: Sounds are all around us. Humans and animals communicate through sound.

What sounds can these children hear in Noisy Town? Make sound effects for each picture below.

Note for parent: Your child can have fun making up sounds to match these pictures.

5

Make sounds for the music in the band.

The triangles in the band go... **ting, ting, ting!**

The drums in the band go... **bong, bong, bong!**

The symbols in the band go... **crash, crash, crash!**

The singers in the band go... **la, la, la!**

... All day long!

Note for parent: You could sing the words to the tune of 'The wheels on the bus go round and round.'

Letter sounds

Each letter of the alphabet has a sound.
Trace over each letter. Start at the red dot and follow the arrows. Say each sound out loud as you write it.

Note for parent: Teachers refer to sounds as 'phonemes'. When we put phonemes together we make words.

7

Say the sounds: s, a, t, p, i

Trace over the letters. Say the sound of each letter.

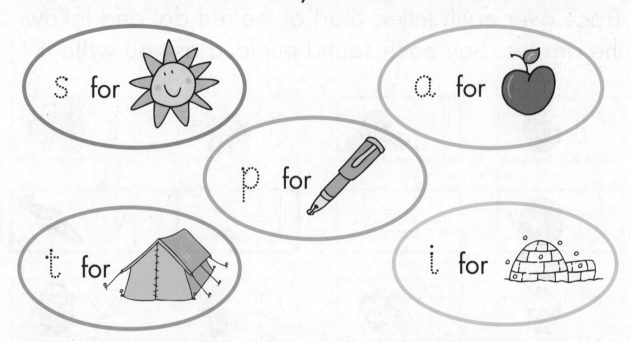

s for

a for

p for

t for

i for

Look at the big picture and name something beginning with each of these sounds:

s a t p i

Note for parent: These are the easiest letters to start with and they are among the most common.

Blend to make words

Blend the letter sounds to find out what Rob Robot is saying. Say the words.

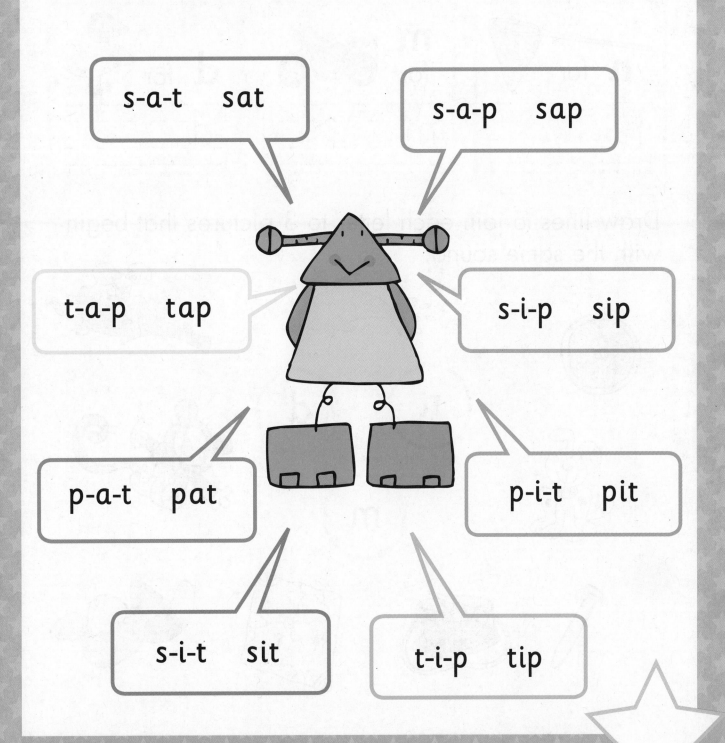

s-a-t sat

s-a-p sap

t-a-p tap

s-i-p sip

p-a-t pat

p-i-t pit

s-i-t sit

t-i-p tip

Note for parent: To 'blend' means to join the separate sounds together until the word 'sounds right'.

Trace over the letters. Say the sound of each letter as you write it.

Draw lines to join each letter to 3 pictures that begin with the same sound.

Note for parent: Help your child to find the correct match, e.g. if they say 'birds' instead of 'nest' then ask, 'Can you think of another word beginning with n?'

Blend to make words

Blend the letter-sounds to read the words on each mat.
Find 2 words that are **exactly** the same.
Draw a circle around them.

nip   pin
mat   tin

din   in
at   and

pan   man
it   did

dad   sad
pad   pan

Now find words that end in the same sound.
Draw lines to join them.

Note for parent: Read aloud the rhyming words with emphasis on the final sounds.
Encourage your child to listen for the rhyme.

Word builder

Letter sounds are put together to build words.
Read the words in each word wall below.

a

a n

a n d

a

a n

a n t

a

a n

p a n

a

a m

S a m

a

a t

p a t

Note for parent: Look for smaller words within longer words, e.g. **am** in **Sam**.
Can you find any little words in your child's name?

Wordsearch

Find 5 words in each wordsearch below. Look across and diagonally. Draw a ring around each word you find in the wordsearch box.

man
sat
tap
tan
map

t	a	p
s	a	t
m	a	n

t	i	p
s	i	t
p	i	n

pin
sit
pip
tin
tip

Note for parent: Word games are a fun way of practising literacy skills.

13

Trace over the letters. Say the sound of each letter as you write it.

Circle 2 pictures in each box that begin with the same sound.

Note for parent: The letters **c** and **k** sound the same in these words. Point out the different sound of **o** in **orange** and **owl**.

Blend to make words

Blend the letter sounds to read the words.

c-a-n   c-a-p   c-o-g

k-i-t   k-i-d   K-i-m

g-o-t   g-a-p   g-a-s

Which of these words has a capital letter? Why?

Note for parent: Tell your child that names begin with capital (or upper-case) letters. Practise writing the capital letter that starts your child's name.

Say the sounds: e, u, r

Trace over the letters. Say the sound of each letter as you write it.

 e for

e _ _ _ _

 u for

u _ _ _ _

 r for

r _ _ _ _

Circle the sound you can hear in the **middle** of each word below.

 pen **e** or **u**

 red **e** or **u**

 sun **e** or **u**

 rug **e** or **u**

 ten **e** or **u**

 cup **e** or **u**

 net **e** or **u**

 nut **e** or **u**

Note for parent: At school, your child will learn how to read words made up of three letters: a consonant, a vowel and a consonant. These are CVC words.

Say the sound: ck

Sometimes we put **c** and **k** together. Blend the letter sounds to find out what Ron Robot is saying. Say the words.

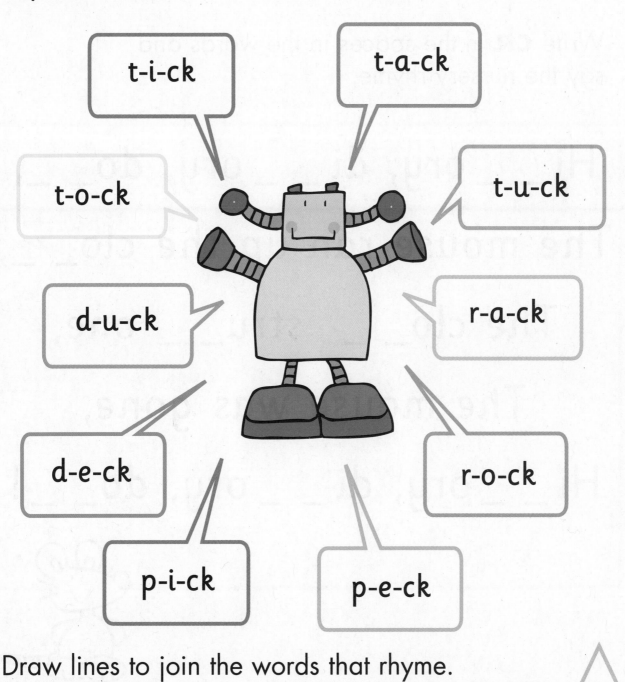

Draw lines to join the words that rhyme.

Note for parent: **ck** is pronounced as one sound. It can also be found in the middle of words, e.g. pocket.

Hickory Dickory Dock

Trace over the letters.

ck   ck   ck   ck   ck

Write **ck** in the spaces in the words and say the nursery rhyme.

Hi _ _ ory, di _ _ ory, do _ _,

The mouse ran up the clo _ _,

The clo _ _ stru _ _ one,

The mouse was gone,

Hi _ _ ory, di _ _ ory, do _ _!

Note for parent: Teach your child some well-known nursery rhymes. The language patterns found within them are a good literacy tool.

Peter Piper

Say this tongue twister as fast you can. Get ready...

Peter Piper picked a peck of pickled peppers!

Where's the peck of pickled peppers Peter Piper picked?

Find all the **p** sounds in this tongue twister and circle each letter **p**.

Here's another one to try. Say it fast!

Red lorry

Yellow lorry!

Note for parent: Do you know any other tongue twisters? Have fun saying them.

19

Say the sounds: l, h, b, f

Trace over the letters. Say the sound of each letter as you write it.

l for

l

h for

h

b for

b

f for

f

Sound out the letters in these words. Read the words.

leg

log

hut

hat

bed

bat

fin

fan

Note for parent: Sound out the letters in each word. Then blend to say the word.

Match letters to pictures

Say the sound of the letter in the middle of each circle. Draw lines to match each letter to 3 pictures in the big circle that begin with this letter.

Note for parent: Prompt your child to find the answer. Praise their efforts. What is obvious to us may not be obvious to a 5-year-old.

21

Blend the sounds together to make words. Draw lines to join the sounds to the complete words. The first one has been done for you.

h - op   fig

f - ig   bit

b - it   mum

t - en   hop

l - ap   ten

m - um   lap

Make some silly words by joining these sounds. Say the words

b - im   t - as   l - ib

s - ut   f - ep   h - of

Note for parent: The silly words are a good test of your child's phonic skills.

Complete the words

Blend the sounds together. Trace the letters to complete the words.

b - at   bat

h - ad   had

b - eg   beg

h - en   hen

b - ig   big

h - id   hid

b - op   bop

h - ot   hot

b - un   bun

h - um   hum

Note for parent: The short vowel sounds of **a**, **e**, **i**, **o** and **u** appear in the words above.

Sound story: ss, ll, ff

Trace over the letters to complete the words.
Say the sounds as you write them.

ss   ll   ff

Ask an adult to read the story to you.

Miss Hill rings the bell.

The class play pass the ball.

Bill falls in the grass.

He hears a hiss!

Then a huff and puff!

"Don't fuss," says Miss Hill.

"But, Miss!" says Bill.

"It's behind you!"

"Run, class!" shouts

Miss Hill.

Note for parent: As you read aloud, point to the words with your finger. Then go back to the text and encourage your child to read the double-letter words.

Tricky words

Blend the letter sounds to read the story.
Say these tricky words:

I   go   no   to   the   of

The bus can **go to the** top **of the** hill.

I can **go to the** top.

I can hop **on the** top.

The dog can run **on the** top.

Oh **no, the** bus hit a rock on **the** top **of the** hill.

Oh **no, the** bus cannot **go**!

Compound words

Join two words to make one word.
Trace over the letters.

sun – set	sunset
sun – tan	suntan
hand – bag	handbag
hill – top	hilltop
up – on	upon
cat – kin	catkin
pad – lock	padlock
ruck – sack	rucksack

Note for parent: These words are known as compound words. There are further examples later in the book.

Grand Old Duke of York

Say the nursery rhyme.

The Grand Old Duke of York,
He had ten thousand men,
He marched them up
to the top of the hill
And he marched them down again....
When they were up they were up,
When they were down they were down.
And when they were only halfway up,
They were neither up nor down!

Where did the Grand Old Duke of York take his men?
Read the signs. Colour in the correct sign.

To the top of the rock

To the big red bus

To the top of the hill

Note for parent: Teach your child some well-known nursery rhymes. The language patterns found within them are a good literacy tool.

27

Read the words underneath each picture.

a pig in the mud

a dog in the sun

a cat in a hat

a rat on the run!

Draw your own picture in the last box to match the last description.

Note for parent: Encourage your child to write captions for their drawings.

Find the word

Look at the pictures and find the correct word to complete each label. Draw lines to join the words.

cats and

pans

bats and

mugs

pots and

eggs

cups and

dogs

hens and

balls

Read the list

Read the items on the list. Tick each one as you find it in Sid's suitcase. Is anything missing?

ball ☐

bell ☐

doll ☐

cup ☐

peg ☐

pen ☐

cap ☐

bat ☐

fan ☐

Circle the item that is on the list but not in his suitcase!

Note for parent: This activity will revise phonemes already introduced.

Circle the correct word to match each picture.

10

| ten | or | den |

| dog | or | cog |

| sip | or | pip |

| fan | or | can |

| mop | or | top |

| sock | or | lock |

Note for parent: This activity will provide further revision of phonemes already introduced.

31

Colour the real words

Say each letter sound, then blend the sounds together to read the word. Which words are silly and which are real? Colour the real words in red.

i-b (ib) a-t (at)

i-f (if)

o-n (on)

u-g (ug)

a-m (am)

u-p (up)

i-n (in)

Note for parent: This activity provides further practice in blending sounds and decoding unfamiliar words.

Name the robots

Say each letter sound, then blend the sounds together to read the words.

Og is from **On**land

Uf is from **Up**land

Ip is from **In**land

Um is from **Ug**land

Who is from **In**land?   Who is from **On**land?

Note for parent: Help your child to spot the difference between the beginning sounds Og and On, etc.

33

Say the sounds: j, v, w, x

Trace over the letters. Say the sound of each letter as you write it.

j for
j

v for
v

w for
w

x for
x

Trace the letters to complete the words.
Read the words.

jar

jug

van

vet

web

witch

box

fox

Note for parent: Few words in the English language begin with **x**. It is more common as a final sound.

Pet names

Match the pets to their owners. Their names start with the same letters. Draw lines to join them.

Jack and... Bix

Raj and... Van

Tim and... Jaws

Pip and... Mug

Vin and... Pop

Bex and... Rav

Meg and... Tom

Note for parent: Alliteration (a string of words with the same beginning sound, e.g. Jack and Jaws) is a common literary device.

Trace over the letters. Say the sound of each letter as you write it.

y for

y

z for

z

zip

yes

zigzag

fizz

zero

buzz

yell

yak

Note for parent: Ask your child which are the last two letters of the alphabet – the answer is **y** and **z**, of course!

Trace over the letters. These two letters make one sound when they are together.

qu   qu   qu

Write **qu** in the spaces in the words and say the rhyme.

Qu is for __ __iver and __ __ake,
But not for shiver and shake,
Qu is for __ __arrel and __ __ibble
But not for dribble and drabble
Qu is for __ __ick and __ __ack,
Queen and __ __iet,
Quarry and __ __ite,
Quiz and __ __est,
Are there any more qu's?
Join the __ __eue!

Note for parent: The letters **q** and **u** are usually found together in the English language.

37

The alphabet

Draw lines to join the letters in alphabetical order from **a** to **z**. Say the alphabet – say the names of the letters, not the sounds.

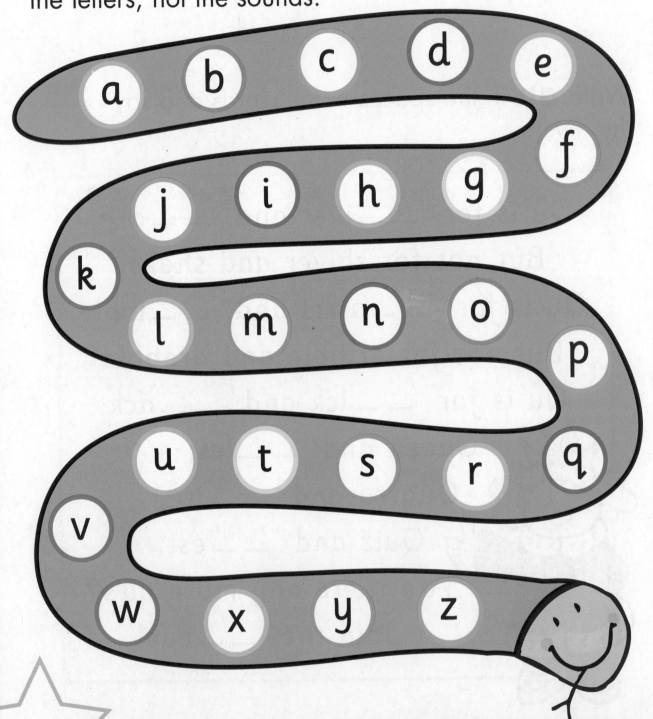

Note for parent: Letter sounds are different from letter names. The sounds are how we pronounce a letter in a word. The name is what we call the letter.

Here are the capital letters. They are used for people's names and the names of countries, towns, rivers, days and months, and much more.

Trace over the capital letters. Start at the red dot and follow the arrows.

Note for parent: Practise writing your child's name in both lower-case (with a capital to start) and upper-case letters.

39

Say the sounds: ch, sh, th

Say the name of each picture. Circle the sound you can hear in each word.

ch or sh

ch or th

ch or sh

th or ch

th or sh

th or ch

Note for parent: This activity introduces common consonant digraphs. A digraph is two letters that together make one sound.

Trace over the letters.

ch   sh   th

Trace the letters to complete the words.
Read the words.

dish

thick

think

shop

chill

ship

chip

rush

thin

wish

chick

shed

Note for parent: These common digraphs can appear at the beginning or the end of words.

41

Tricky words

Say these tricky words. They are not easy to sound out so you just have to learn them by sight. They are important because we use them a lot!

he

she

we

be

my

me

you

they

all

are

was

her

Note for parent: There is no easy way of learning these words. But with practice and familiarity your child will begin to recognise them on sight.

Read the speech balloons

Read the speech balloons to find out what they are saying.

Note for parent: What do you think the children are talking about? Encourage your child to think of possible scenarios.

43

Blend the sounds to read the words below.
The first two letters make one sound.

For example: **fr-o-g**

Try these:

cr-a-b

fr-e-t

gl-u-m

gr-i-t

gr-a-b

tr-o-ll

sn-u-b

sn-u-g

Note for parent: The first two letters in these words are consonant digraphs.
Together they make one sound.

Blend the sounds to read the words below. The last two letters make one sound.

For example: **j-u-mp**

Try these:

l-a-mp

y-e-lp

s-i-nk

c-a-rd

d-i-sk

b-u-mp

s-o-ft

d-e-sk

Note for parent: The last two letters in these words are consonant digraphs. Together they make one sound.

45

Read this story with an adult. Try to read some of the words yourself. When you come to a picture, predict what the word might be.

Once upon a time **3** [goat] s

had to cross a [bridge].

Trit-trot, trit-trot, went the [goat] s.

A troll jumped onto the [bridge].

"I am a troll, fol-de-rol!

Get off my [bridge]

or I will eat you all!" said the troll.

The biggest [goat] said, "No, you will not!"

and butted the troll off the [bridge]!

The **3** [goat] s crossed the [bridge] safely

and lived happily ever after.

Note for parent: Encourage your child to try to read some of the words they have already met in this book.

Rhyme time

Blend the sounds in the words and try to read the poem yourself.

cl-i-p, cl-o-p

b-i-ng, b-o-ng,

tr-i-t, tr-o-t

d-i-ng, d-o-ng,

t-i-ck, t-o-ck

s-i-ng, s-o-ng,

p-i-ng, p-o-ng!

Word builder

Make some silly words by joining these sounds.
Say the words.

lu - nd

th - ad

ve - nk

te - th

ch - om

pe - sh

sa - th

zi - ch

bi - sh

gl - ub

Note for parent: Reading these silly words is a useful test of your child's phonics skills.

Vowels and consonants

The alphabet has 5 vowels. They are: **a, e, i, o, u**. Find the vowels and colour them in red. The other letters are called consonants. Colour these in a different colour.

Write your name in the space below – with each letter in a circle. Colour the vowels in your name in red and the consonants in another colour.

○ ○ ○ ○ ○ ○ ○ ○ ○ ○

Note for parent: Your child needs to know what the vowels and consonants are. Most words in the English language contain vowels and consonants.

Say the sound of the letters in the middle of each box. Draw lines to connect the sound to two pictures in the box that contain this sound.

Note for parent: Occasionally you may need to prompt your child to come up with the right connections.

Trace over the letters.

ng   nd   st

Trace the letters to complete the words.
Read the words.

fang

rung

song

stand

bend

land

rust

test

chest

Say the sounds: wh, ph

Say the sounds of the letters. Trace over the letters.

wh for

wh _ _ _ _ _

ph for

ph _ _ _ _ _

photo

graph

whip

phone

whim

whizz

whale

when

white

whisk

phonics

wheel

The **wh** sound begins lots of question words: what, when, where, why?

Note for parent: Point out that the digraph **ph** sounds like **f**.

Silly words

Blend the letter sounds to read these silly words.

whib

bliff

whon

gloff

phem

enuff

blaph

crelf

Note for parent: Reading these silly words is a useful test of your child's phonics skills.

Say the sounds: ai, a-e

Blend the letter sounds **a** and **i** to read these words.

r-ai-n

ch-ai-n

tr-ai-n

These words have the same long sound of **a** but are spelt differently.

m-ane

pl-ane

cr-ane

Draw lines to join each picture to a word.

snail   lake   gate   snake

Note for parent: Listen for the long sound of **a** in these words.

Sounds the same

Words can sound the same but have different meanings.

For example:

> A squirrel has a long **tail**.
>
> This is a fairy**tale** book.

Circle the words that sound the same but have different meanings.

> Tim has a pain in his knee.
>
> This is a window pane.

> A town has a main street.
>
> A male lion has a mane.

Note for parent: Words that sound the same but are spelt differently and have different meanings are called 'homophones'. There are more examples later in the book.

55

Trace over the letters.

ay   ay   ay

Trace the letters to complete the words.
Read the poem.

Boat in the bay
Pay day
Mouse in the hay
May day
Sun's rays
This way
I say
Let's play!

Trace over the letters to complete the names of the days. Read the poem.

Monday's child is fair of face,

Tuesday's child is full of grace,

Wednesday's child is full of woe,

Thursday's child has far to go,

Friday's child is loving and giving,

Saturday's child works hard for a living,

But the child that was born on

Sunday is happy, smiling and

has lots to say!

Note for parent: Tell your child the day on which they were born. Do they think the rhyme could be true? Discuss this together.

57

Say the sounds: *ee, ea*

The letter-sounds **ee** and **ea** often sound the same. For example:

I can see a spider.

I can see the sea!

They sound the same but have different meanings.

Say this rhyme.

A sailor went to the sea sea sea,

To see what he could see see see,

But all that he could see see see,

Was the bottom of the

deep blue sea sea sea!

Note for parent: Follow the words with your finger. Point out that **see** and **sea** sound the same but are spelt differently.

Nonsense rhyme

Read this nonsense rhyme. Listen for the sounds **ee** and **ea**. Circle them all. Can you find all five?

> There was a young girl called Jean
>
> Who wanted to look like a bean.
>
> She dressed in red and everyone said,
>
> "Beans are meant to be green!"

Draw pictures to match these words.

a cream cake	a neat seat	a dream team
a shark's teeth	a sheep's feet	a sweet treat

Note for parent: **ea** in **meant** is a short sound, but in **Jean**, and **bean(s)** it is a long sound.

59

Say the sound: ea (short sound)

Trace over the letters.

ea   ea   ea

Write the letters **ea** in the spaces to complete the words. Read the words.

sleepy h__d

brown br__d

light as a f__ther

blue thr__d

winter w__ther

green m__dow

Draw the missing pictures to match the words.

Note for parent: Compare the short sound of **ea** in head with the long sound of **ea** in cream.

Say the sound: i-e

The **e** at the end of these words changes **i** from a short sound into a long sound.

Say these words:

pin – pine	pip – pipe

Write **e** at the end of the words then read them aloud.

spik__

slic__

ric__

mik__

lik__

ic__

bik__

hik__

nic__

trik__

Note for parent: Sometimes the **e** at the end of these words is called magic **e** because it changes the sound of the vowel that comes before it.

Magic e

Write **e** at the end of these words to make new words.

plum__

spin__

ton__

rob__

can__

cap__

cut__

cub__

plan__

tap__

hug__

tub__

Note for parent: Here are more examples of magic **e**.

Trace over the letters.

igh **as in night**

y **as in sky**

Trace the letters to complete the words.
Blend the sounds to read the words.

high   sky   might   cry

my   sigh   tight

fry   sight

try   dry   right

Note for parent: Listen for the long **igh/y** sound in these words.

63

Write the letters **ight** in the spaces to complete the words in the poem.

Fright night!

Late last n _ _ _ _ ,

I had a fr _ _ _ _,

I turned on the l _ _ _ _,

The sky was br_ _ _ _,

I pulled the covers t _ _ _ _,

And hid from s _ _ _ _,

Thunder and l _ _ _ _ ning

Is so fr _ _ _ _ ening!

Then out came the morning sun

With golden boxing gloves on,

The sun won the f _ _ _ _,

Everything was alr _ _ _ _.

Answer the questions

Read the questions. Circle **yes** or **no**.

Can a duck read?　　yes　no

Can a dog cry?　　yes　no

Can a cat play bingo?　　yes　no

Can a jelly wobble?　　yes　no

Can you ride a bike?　　yes　no

Can you say a rhyme?　　yes　no

Can ice melt?　　yes　no

Can the sun freeze?　　yes　no

Trace over the letters to write the sounds in the words. Read the captions. Draw the missing pictures.

billy goat

long coat

warty toad

rowing boat

deep snow

dog show

bow and arrow

flower growing

Note for parent: Notice 'flower' is a different **ow** sound.

Say the sounds: oa, o-e

Read the words on the stones. Find a path across the river by colouring in words that rhyme with **stone**.

Note for parent: Some of these words are nonsense or silly words, i.e. **fon**, **hon** – they don't rhyme with **stone**. However, **moan** and **groan** do rhyme.

67

Say the sounds: oo, ou, u

Trace over the letters to write the sounds in the words.
Read the captions. Draw the missing pictures.

Good book

Take a look

I can cook

Big truck

Best of luck

Beans and jelly – yuk!

Trace over the letters to write the sounds in the words.
Read what the children are saying.

I could.

He would.

You should!

Note for parent: The pronunciation of words such as book will vary due to different regional accents.

Different books

Read the names of these different types of books.
Tick the ones that you have at home.

cookbook ☐

workbook ☐

sketchbook ☐

scrapbook ☐

textbook ☐

notebook ☐

storybook ☐

handbook ☐

Note for parent: Identify these types of books. Show examples if you have them at home.

Read the words. Listen for the different sounds of **ar** and **or** in these words.

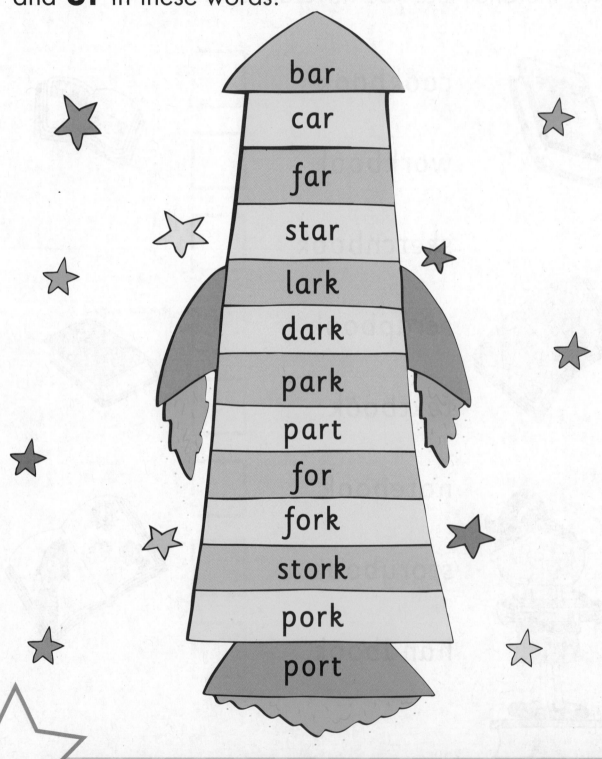

bar
car
far
star
lark
dark
park
part
for
fork
stork
pork
port

Note for parents: Help your child to read these words. Follow the words with your finger.
Listen for the differences.

Say the sounds: ore, oor, oar, aw

Write the missing letters to make these words.

| core | score | store | shore | floor | door |

front d _ _ _

apple c _ _ _

clean fl _ _ _

food st _ _ _

sea sh _ _ _

big sc _ _ _ 100

Write **oar** and **aw** in these words:

wild b_ _ _ and lion's r_ _ _!

dog's p_ _ and shark's j_ _!

Note for parent: Point out that these letter endings look different but they sound the same, though in some regional accents they may differ.

Tricky words

Read and try to remember what these tricky words look like.

Note for parent: There is no easy way of learning these words. But with practice and familiarity your child will begin to recognise them on sight.

Which is correct? Circle the correct word.

sed or **said**

soe or **so**

some or som

com or **come**

hav or **have**

like or lyke

littel or **little**

there or thare

Note for parent: This activity will help your child to recognise tricky words.

73

Draw lines to join the words that sound the same.

hare stair fair pear bear

stare pair bare hair fare

Write the correct words in the captions below.

long _ _ _ _   fluffy _ _ _ _

a _ _ _ _ of shoes

a _ _ _ _ tree

Note for parent: Words such as **fare**, **hare**, **stare** are sometimes called magic **e** words because the final **e** changes the sound of the vowel that comes before it.

Choose the correct word to match each definition.
Copy the word into the space.

mare

square

highchair

footwear

nightmare

swimwear

A four-sided shape _____

A chair for babies _____

A female horse _____

A bad dream _____

Clothes for swimming _____

Boots, shoes and sandals _____

Note for parent: The endings **mare**, **wear** and **air** are rhyming in these words.

75

Say the sound: er

Draw lines to join the labels to the people in the photograph. Who do you think they are?

Choose from the following words:

mother	father	brother

sister	grandfather	grandmother

Compound words

Some words are made by joining two words together.
Draw lines to join two words to make a new word.

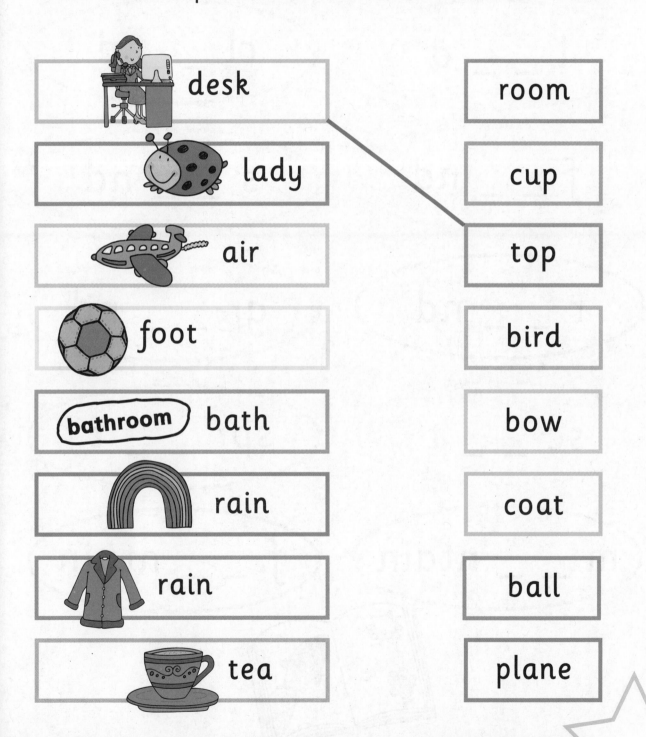

desk	room
lady	cup
air	top
foot	bird
bath	bow
rain	coat
rain	ball
tea	plane

Note for parent: Look out for other examples of compound words.

77

Write the **ou** sounds in the words. Read the words.

l _ _ d

cl _ _ d

f _ _ nd

s _ _ nd

r _ _ nd

gr _ _ nd

sc _ _ t

spr _ _ t

m _ _ ntain

f _ _ ntain

Note for parent: These are examples of the long sound of **ou**. Compare them with **ou** in **could** on page 68, which is a short sound.

What is...?

Read each question and choose a word from the list below. Write the word on the line.

cloud	round	sprout
fountain	ground	found

What is green all over and good for you? _____

What is white, grey or black and floats above you? _____

What is the opposite of lost? _____

What is wet and watery, and goes up and down? _____

What is under your feet? _____

What is a ball shape? _____

Note for parent: Help your child to think of words that use the short sound for **ou** such as **would**.

79

Say the sounds: oi, oy

Trace over the letters.

oi   oy

Trace the letters to complete the words.
Read the words.

Note for parent: **o** comes before **i**. Compare with **kiosk**, which is a different sound.

Match the definitions

Choose a word to fit each definition.
Write it in the space.

boil   soil   spoil   coin   voice   oil   join

You might put this in your car. _____

You do this to water to make
it hot. _____

You plant seeds in this. _____

You use this to pay
for things. _____

You ruin something. _____

You put things together. _____

You use this to speak. _____

Tricky words

Read and try to remember what these tricky words look like.

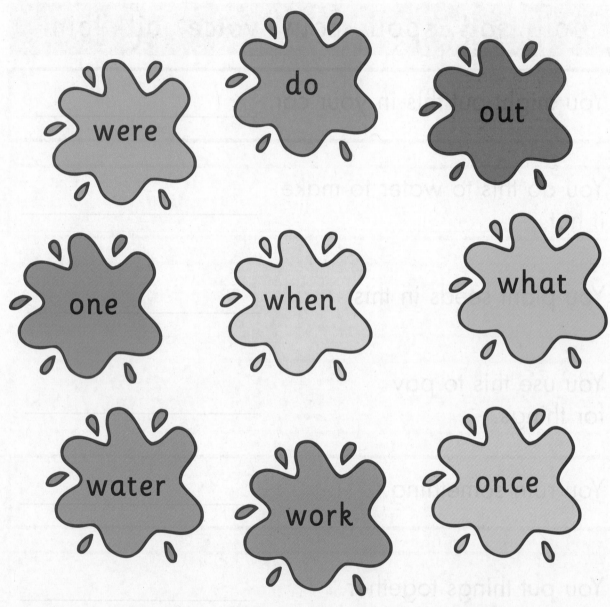

You can test how well you have remembered them on the opposite page. First, you must cover this page.

Note for parent: There is no easy way of learning these words. But with practice and familiarity your child will begin to recognise them on sight.

Tricky test

Which is correct? Circle the correct word.

were or weur

duw or do

owt or out

wone or one

wen or when

whot or what

water or worter

werk or work

wonce or once

Note for parent: Help your child to recognise the correct spellings of these tricky words.

83

Trace the letters to complete the words.
Read the words.

crew

blue

tune

moon

spoon

stew

flute

tube

noon

balloon

Note for parent: These are long vowel sounds.

Draw lines to join words that rhyme.

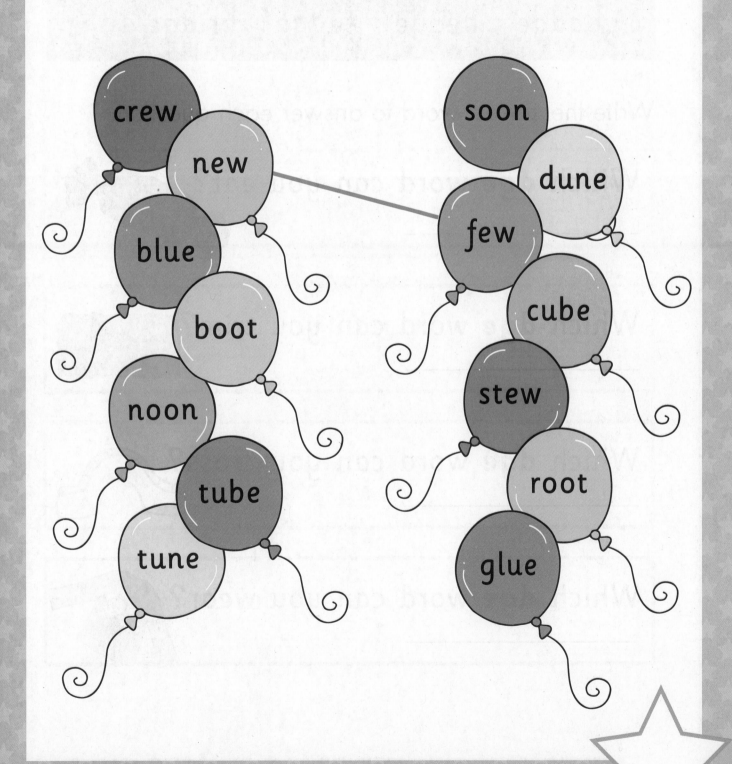

Note for parent: Emphasise the ends of the words as you read them.

85

Say the sound: dge

Read the words below.

badge   hedge   fudge   bridge

Write the correct word to answer each question.

Which **dge** word can you eat?

_____

Which **dge** word can you trim?

_____

Which **dge** word can you cross?

_____

Which **dge** word can you wear?

_____

Note for parent: These three letters are called a consonant trigraph. Together they make one sound.

Sound story: g, t

Read the story. Listen for the sounds of **g** and **t**.

One day a huge giant met a tall giraffe.

"I am the tallest creature in the land!" said the giant.

"I can touch the sky if I want to!"

"You are not taller than me!" said the giraffe.

"I can touch the tops of the trees with my tongue!"

"I can do that too!" said the giant.

Just then a tiny ant scuttled at their feet.

"I can touch the top of that mountain," said the ant.

The huge giant and the tall giraffe both laughed.

"No, you can't!" they said.

Then the tiny ant ran up the mountain to the very top!

"Told you so!" said the tiny ant.

Note for parent: Read the story together. Follow the words with your finger and emphasise the sounds **g** and **t**. Notice that **giraffe** and **giant** have the same sound.

87

Say the sound: le

Read the words. Choose a word to fit each definition. Write it in the space.

> little   bottle   kettle   settle
> nettle   rattle   cattle

You boil water in it. _____

You can get a red rash from it. _____

Provide us with milk and meat. _____

Not big. _____

It holds liquid. _____

Baby's noisy toy. _____

Note for parent: The double **t** sound is commonly followed by **le**.

Hey, Diddle, Diddle

Say the nursery rhyme.

Hey, diddle, diddle,
The cat and the fiddle,
The cow jumped over the moon.
The little dog laughed to see such fun,
And the dish ran away with the spoon!

Trace over the letters to complete the words.
Read the words.

middle   riddle   toddle   muddle

huddle   cuddle   puddle   paddle

Note for parent: Teach your child some well-known nursery rhymes. The language patterns found within them are a good literacy tool.

Read the rhyme

Say the rhyme. Listen for repeated sounds.

> Hubble, bubble,
> Toil and trouble,
> Fire burn and cauldron bubble!

Now read the words in the cauldron. Some are silly words!

pubble

jubble

stubble

zubble

gubble

rubble

tubble

vubble

cubble

wubble

mubble

Note for parent: Reading silly words is a good test of your child's phonics skills.

Rhyming wheels

Draw lines to join words that rhyme with the word in the middle of the wheel.

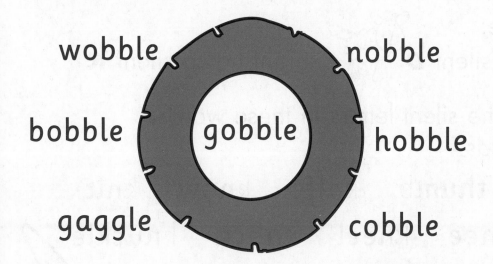

wobble   nobble

bobble   gobble   hobble

gaggle   cobble

tumble   humble

jumble   bumble   rumble

goggle   mumble

Which words do not rhyme? _____

Write them here: _____

Note for parent: Discuss why **gaggle** and **goggle** don't rhyme with the other words in the wheels.

91

Silent letters: b, k

Some words have silent letters that are not pronounced when we say the word.

For example:
lamb has a silent **b**   knight has a silent **k**

Trace over the silent letters in these words.
Say the words.

comb   thumb   knife   know   knit

knot   knee   kneel   knock   knuckle

Choose from the words above to complete these sentences.

We cut food with a _____ .

We neaten our hair with a _____ .

We tie a _____ in string.

We _____ with knitting needles.

We _____ and understand.

We _____ on our knees.

We _____ on the door.

Note for parent: Together think of more silent letter words.

Silent letters: g, w

Trace over the silent letters in these words.
Say the words.

gnaw   gnome   gnat   write   wrist

wrong   wrap   wreck   wrestle   wriggle

Join the words to the definition.

A garden ornament   (gnaw)

A small biting insect   (wrong)

A join in the arm   (write)

Not right   (gnat)

To make words   (gnome)

To bite and chew   (wrist)

But... we do sound out the **g** in **gnu**!

Note for parent: Together think of more silent letter words.

93

Trace over the **y** endings to complete the words.
Read the words.

hair**y**   scar**y**   happ**y**
bon**y**   funn**y**   sunn**y**

Choose a word from the list above to fit each caption. Write the word in the space.

A _____ day

A _____ birthday

A _____ clown

A _____ goat

A _____ skeleton

A _____ monster

Note for parent: Older children in the age group may know that describing words such as these are called adjectives.

More y endings

Trace over the **y** endings to complete the words.
Read the words.

mummy   daddy   baby

puppy   fairy   bunny

Choose a word from the list above to fit each caption. Write the word in the space.

A happy _____

A messy _____

A silly _____

A busy _____

A pretty _____

A fluffy _____

Note for parent: Think of alternative adjectives for these pictures.

95

Sounding and blending

Sound out the letters. Then blend the sounds to read the words

For example: **dr-i-nk**

br-u-sh

fr-o-st

ch-e-st

st-a-mp

cr-i-sp

pr-i-nt

cl-a-ng

th-a-nk

Note for parent: If the word doesn't 'sound right', encourage your child to try again or suggest what the word might be.

Silly sounds

Try these silly sounds. Blend them together to read the words.

bl-u-nk

tw-u-st

fr-i-nt

fl-e-nd

gr-e-nt

dr-o-st

cr-a-nd

sw-i-sk

Note for parent: Reading these silly words is a good test of your child's phonics skills.

97

Read and try to remember what these tricky words look like.

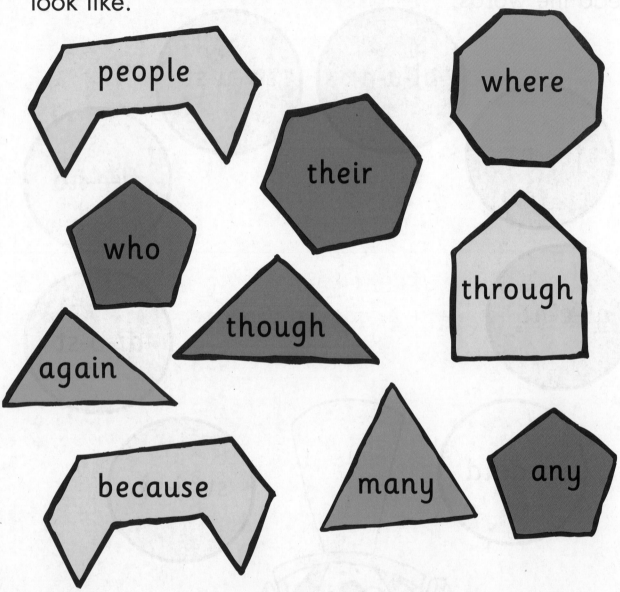

people

where

their

who

through

though

again

because

many

any

You can test how well you have remembered them on the opposite page. First, you must cover this page.

Note for parent: There is no easy way of learning these words. But with practice and familiarity your child will begin to recognise them on sight.

Which is correct? Circle the correct word.

peeple or **people**

thair or **their**

where or **weer**

who or **whu**

agen or **again**

thow or **though**

thruw or **through**

meny or **many**

becus or **because**

any or **eny**

Note for parent: This activity will support your child in identifying tricky words.

99

Say the sound: tch

Trace over the beginning sounds to complete these words. Draw the missing pictures.

ca**tch**

ma**tch**

wa**tch**

fe**tch**

wi**tch**

swi**tch**

hu**tch**

ha**tch**

sa**tch**el

ki**tch**en

Note for parents: **tch** is a consonant trigraph. Try to think of further examples of this trigraph to add to the list.

Blending two halves

Blend the two halves of each word together. Say the word then write it in the space.

spr – int	sprint
str – ing	
str – ong	
str – eam	
str – eet	
scr – ew	
scr – ape	
scr – eam	
shr – imp	
sti – tch	

Note for parent: At this stage, we can split these words neatly into two halves to aid blending.

101

Complete the signs. Write the missing letters in the spaces.

K _ _ P OFF THE GRA _ _

E _ IT

D _ NGER KEEP OU _!

WE _ PAIN _

_ OILETS

TOWN CEN _ RE

Note for parent: Read road and street signs when you are out and about together.

Silly signs

Read the silly signs from Ugland. Can you spot the spelling mistakes? Write the correct spellings underneath.

WELCUM TO UGLAND

_____

UM'S HOWSE

_____

RIVAR UG

_____

UG MUG'S TEE SHOP

_____

KAR PARK

_____

UGLAND ERRPORT

_____

Say the sound: tion

Blend the sounds. Say the words.

sta-tion	station
cap-tion	caption
rel-a-tion	relation
loc-a-tion	location
edu-ca-tion	education
imag-in-a-tion	imagination
exam-in-a-tion	examination

Choose a word above to complete each sentence.

The train arrives at the _____ .

My school gives me an _____ .

I use my _____ when I write a story.

Members of my family are my _____ s.

Note for parent: Discuss the meanings of these words and give examples.

Blend the sounds to read the words on the book covers.

picture book

fun adventures

creepy creatures

nature

in the future

Which type of book do you like best?
Copy the title in the space below.

_____

Note for parent: Help your child to sound out and read these words. Discuss what might be inside the book.

105

Plurals

When there is more than one of something, this is called a plural.

For example: **kittens**

Make these words plural by writing **s** at the end.

dog_	hat_
flower_	star_
tree_	chair_
book_	umbrella_

But... if a word ends in **ch**, **sh**, **s** or **x** we add **es**. Add **es** to these words.

watch_ _	box _ _
dish_ _	glass_ _
patch _ _	splash _ _
fox _ _	kiss _ _

Note for parent: Some words don't change in the plural, e.g. **sheep**, **deer**. The plural for **fish** can be **fish** or **fishes** – both are acceptable.

More plurals

If a word ends in **y**, the plural ending becomes **ies**.

For example: **baby   babies**

Add **ies** to complete these plural words.

fairy   fair_ _ _

pony   pon _ _ _

lorry   lorr _ _ _

Some words end in **ves** in the plural.

knife   kni _ _ _

wife   wi _ _ _

life   li _ _ _

Note for parent: Discuss other exception words that your child might
know, e.g. **foot – feet**, **tooth – teeth**.

107

Verbs: ing endings

When a verb ends in **ing** it tells us that the action is happening now.

For example: fly ➞ fly**ing**

Add **ing** to these words. Write them in the spaces.

eat _ _ _   jump_ _ _   crawl_ _ _

But… if a word ends in **e**, we drop the **e** before adding **ing**.

For example: dive ➞ diving

Add **ing** to these words. Write them in the spaces.

dance   danc_ _ _   bake   bak_ _ _

race   rac_ _ _   ride   rid_ _ _

skate   skat_ _ _   wave   wav_ _ _

                           write   writ_ _ _

More ing endings

If a word has a vowel before the final consonant, we double the consonant before adding **ing**.

For example: run ➡ runn**ing**

Double the consonant and add **ing** to these words. Write in the spaces.

 skip_ _ _ _ _

hop_ _ _ _ _

 swim_ _ _ _ _

dig_ _ _ _ _

 cut_ _ _ _ _

clap_ _ _ _ _

 drip_ _ _ _ _

drum_ _ _ _ _

Note for parent: Think of more examples that follow this rule in the simple present tense.

109

Verbs: ed endings

When a verb ends in **ed** it tells us that the action happened in the past.

For example: **play** → **played**

Add **ed** to these words. Write them in the spaces.

walk_ _   look_ _   cook_ _

push_ _   pull_ _   help_ _ _

Double the consonant and add **ed** to these words.

skip_ _ _   shop_ _ _

Note for parent: Think of more examples of past tense verbs ending in **ed**.

Exception words

Some past tense verbs don't follow the rules.
Read them and learn to spell them.

say   said

run   ran

swim   swam

sing   sang

fly   flew

dig   dug

write   wrote

draw   drew

drink   drank

read   read

Note for parent: Learn to spell these exwords by first looking at them, then covering them, then writing them out and, finally, checking the spelling.

111

er endings

Add **er** to these words to find out what people do.
If the word ends in **e**, e.g. dance, then just add **r**.

read_ _   teach_ _   dance_

climb_ _   play_ _   paint_ _

write_   bake_   sing_ _

Note for parent: There are many more – together you could make a list of further examples.

More words with er

If a word has a vowel before the final consonant, we double the consonant before adding **er**.

For example:

swim ➡ swim**mer**

run _ _ _

jog _ _ _

drum _ _ _

swim _ _ _

thin _ _ _

fat _ _ _

Note for parent: Words such as **smaller** and **taller** have a similar spelling pattern.

113

Draw lines to join **what** was said to **how** it was said.

"I have lost,"

the toddler said sleepily.

"They stole it!"

the dog barked playfully.

"We want more!"

we said angrily.

"I want to go to bed,"

she said sadly.

"Woof! Woof!"

they said greedily.

Note for parent: This activity introduces adverbs – which tell us more about the verb in the sentence.

Suffix: ness

Add the suffix **ness** to the following words.

loud_ _ _ _   playful_ _ _ _

cheap_ _ _ _   late_ _ _ _

sick_ _ _ _   sad_ _ _ _

great_ _ _ _   smooth_ _ _ _

If a word ends in **y**, you need to change the **y** to **i** before adding **ness**.

For example: **happy** ➡ **happiness**

clumsy ➡ clums_ _ _ _ _

Choose from the words above to complete each sentence.

The _____ of the thunder scared us all.

Kittens are known for their _____ .

Some people get travel _____ .

She cried with _____ when she won.

Note for parent: Refer to the last sentence and discuss why people may sometimes 'cry with happiness'.

115

Introducing syllables

Count the syllables (or beats) in these words as you sound them out.

For example: **dog** has one syllable.
el/e/phant has three.

Draw lines in the words to separate the syllables.

umbrella

snowman

spider

mug

jellyfish

wardrobe

holiday

octopus

Note for parent: Use the word 'beat' instead of syllable, if you prefer, and count the beats in each word as you sound it out.

Clap our names

Read the names on the school register. Clap the syllables in each name.

For example: **Cin/de/rell/a** has four beats!

Ali	Mohammad
Ella	Nazeem
Isabella	Oliver
Jim	Poppy
Katya	Harry

Note for parent: Try your child's name first. Do you know any longer names? Rumpelstiltskin has four!

117

Read and try to remember what these tricky words look like.

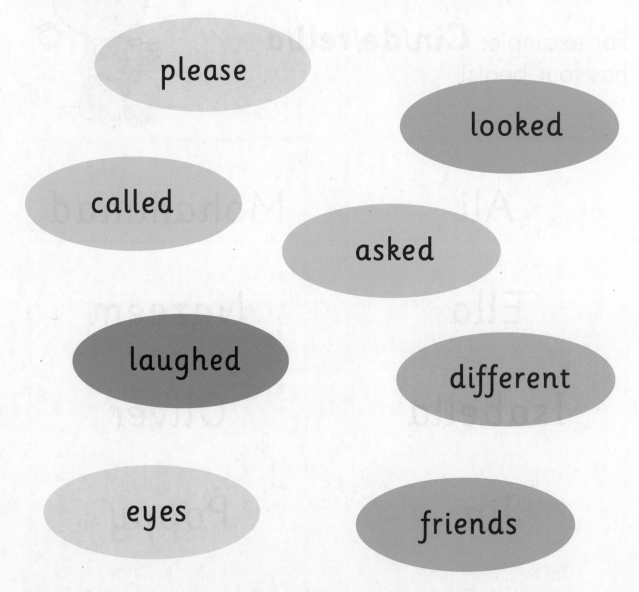

please

looked

called

asked

laughed

different

eyes

friends

You can test how well you have remembered them on the opposite page. First, you must cover this page.

Note for parent: There is no easy way of learning these words. But with practice and familiarity your child will begin to recognise them on sight.

Tricky test

Which is correct? Circle the correct word.

pleese or **please**

lucked or **looked**

called or cawled

asked or askt

laught or **laughed**

different or differant

eyes or eiys

friends or frends

Note for parent: This activity will help your child revise some tricky words that are commonly misspelt.

119

Prefix: un

The prefix **un** changes the root word to its opposite.

lucky → **un**lucky

Write **un** before the start of these words.

_ _well	_ _tidy
_ _even	_ _fair
_ _happy	_ _kind

Choose words from the list above to complete these sentences.

Cinderella was _____ because the stepsisters were _____ to her.

She had to do all the housework.

It was _____.

The stepsisters were very _____.

They left all their clothes for Cinderella to pick up!

Note for parent: Discuss which words will best fit in the spaces.

Prefix: re

If we put **re** before a verb it means the action will happen again.

For example: **re**do – to do again

Write **re** before these verbs.

_ _ pay	_ _ mix
_ _ fill	_ _ fuel
_ _ think	_ _ wind
_ _ name	_ _ call

Note for parent: Discuss the meanings of these words and try to think of examples from your child's own experiences.

121

Sounds the same

Some words sound the same but are spelt differently and mean different things.

Read these words:

mail – male

plaice – place

new – knew

sow – sew

witch – which

threw – through

Choose a word from the list above to complete each sentence. Write the word in the space.

I have _____ school shoes.
A boy is a _____ child.
The _____ flew on a broomstick.
It was a fun _____ to visit.
She _____ the ball.

Note for parent: These words are more examples of homophones – words that sound the same but are spelt differently and have different meanings.

Sounds the same: wordsearch

Find 21 homophones in the wordsearch. Look across and down. Draw a ring around each word you find.

b	p	l	a	c	e	s	s	v	s
n	l	d	d	w	h	e	r	e	o
m	a	i	l	m	a	l	e	e	w
a	i	d	t	w	e	r	e	t	w
i	c	t	h	r	o	u	g	h	r
n	e	h	e	t	a	i	l	r	w
m	t	e	i	c	z	z	n	e	i
a	d	r	r	d	k	n	e	w	t
n	w	e	a	r	s	e	w	b	c
e	t	a	l	e	w	h	i	c	h

tail tale mail male main mane
sow sew witch which their there
threw through place plaice new
knew where were wear

Answers

Page 8
s for sun and snail, a for aeroplane, t for tree, p for parrot, i for insect

Page 10
n for net,
m for motorbike,
d for duck,
n – nest, nuts, nail;
m – map, monkey, mushroom;
d – dolphin, dog, drum

Page 11
pan and pan are exactly the same.
mat – at,
pin – tin – din – in,
pan – man,
dad – sad – pad

Page 13

Page 14
g – goat, gate;
o – orange, owl;
c – car, cup;
k – kite, key

Page 16
e for egg,
u for umbrella,
r for robot
pen, red, sun, rug, ten, cup, net, nut

Page 17
tick – pick, tack – rack, tuck – duck, rock – tock, peck – deck

Page 18
Hickory, dickory, dock,
The mouse ran up the clock,
The clock struck one,
The mouse was gone,
Hickory, dickory, dock!

Page 19
Peter Piper picked a peck of pickled peppers!

Where's the peck of pickled peppers Peter Piper picked?

Page 20
l for leaf, h for horse, b for bag, f for fox

Page 21
l – ladder, leaf, lion,
h – hat, hen, house,
b – bat, bed, bus,
f – feather, fish, fly

Page 22
h-op – hop, f-ig – fig, b-it – bit, t-en – ten, l-ap – lap, m-um – mum

Page 27
To the top of the hill

Page 29
cats and dogs,
bats and balls,
pots and pans,
cups and mugs,
hens and eggs

Page 30
The doll is not in his suitcase!

Page 31
ten, dog, pip, fan, mop, lock

Page 32
Real words – at, on, am, in, up, if

Page 33
Ip is from Inland, Og is from Onland

Page 34
j for jelly, v for vase, w for watch, x for x-ray

Page 35
Jack and Jaws, Raj and Rav, Tim and Tom, Pip and Pop, Vin and Van, Bex and Bix, Meg and Mug

Page 36
y for yo-yo, z for zebra

Page 37
quiver, quake, quarrel, quibble, quick, quack, quiet, quite, quest, queue

Page 38
a, b, c, d, e, f, g, h, i, j, k, l, m, n, o, p, q, r, s, t, u, v, w, x, y, z

Page 40
shell, chin, fish, chimp, teeth, church

Page 46
three, goats, bridge

Page 50
ng – king, ring, nd – hand, sand, st – step, star

Page 52
wh for whale, ph for phone

Page 54

snail lake gate snake

Page 55
pain and pane, main and mane

Page 59
Jean, bean, beans, be, green
(ea in meant is a different sound)

Page 60
head, bread, feather, thread, weather, meadow

Page 61
spike, rice, slice, mike, ice, bike, like, hike, nice, trike

Page 62
plume, spine, tone, robe, cane, cape, cute, huge, plane, tape, cube, tube

Page 64
night, fright, light, bright, tight, sight, lightning, frightening, fight, alright

Page 67
stone, bone, cone, moan, phone, groan, throne, zone, tone, ozone

Answers

Page 71
front door, apple core,
clean floor, food store,
sea shore, big score
wild boar, lion's roar,
dog's paw, shark's jaw

Page 73
said, so, some,
come, have, like,
little, there

Page 74
hare – hair,
stair – stare,
fair – fare,
pear – pair,
bear – bare
long hair,
fluffy hare,
a pair of shoes,
a pear tree

Page 75
square, highchair,
mare, nightmare,
swimwear, footwear

Page 76

brother

sister

mother

father

grandmother

grandfather

Page 77
desktop, ladybird,
airplane, football,
bathroom, rainbow,
raincoat, teacup

Page 78
loud, cloud, found,
sound, round,
ground, scout, sprout,
mountain, fountain

Page 79
sprout, cloud,
found, fountain,
ground, round

Page 81
oil, boil, soil, coin,
spoil, join, voice

Page 83
were, do, out,
one, when, what,
water, work, once

Page 85
crew – stew – new – few,
blue – glue, boot – root,
noon – soon – tune –
dune, tube – cube

Page 86
fudge, hedge, bridge,
badge

Page 88
kettle, nettle, cattle, little,
bottle, rattle

Page 91
gobble – wobble,
cobble, nobble,
hobble, bobble,
bumble – humble
rumble, mumble, jumble,
tumble
gaggle and goggle do
not rhyme

Page 92
knife, comb, knot, knit, know, kneel, knock

Page 93
A garden ornament – gnome
A small biting insect – gnat
A join in the arm – wrist
Not right – wrong
To make words – write
To bite and chew – gnaw

Page 94
A sunny day
A happy birthday
A funny clown
A hairy goat
A bony skeleton
A scary monster

Page 95
A happy baby
A messy puppy
A silly daddy
A busy mummy
A pretty fairy
A fluffy bunny

Page 99
people, their, where, who, again, though, through, many, because, any

Page 101
string, strong, stream, street, screw, scrape, scream, shrimp, stitch

Page 102
KEEP OFF THE GRASS, EXIT, DANGER KEEP OUT!, WET PAINT, TOILETS, TOWN CENTRE

Page 103
WELCOME, HOUSE, RIVER, TEA, CAR, AIRPORT

Page 104
station, education, imagination, relations

Page 106
dogs, hats, flowers, stars, trees, chairs, books, umbrellas
watches, boxes, dishes, glasses, patches, splashes, foxes, kisses

Page 107
fairies, ponies, lorries, knives, wives, lives

Page 108
eating, jumping, crawling
dancing, baking, racing, riding, skating, waving, writing

Page 109
skipping, hopping, swimming, digging, cutting, clapping, dripping, drumming

Page 110
walked, looked, cooked, pushed, pulled, helped, skipped, shopped

Page 112
reader, teacher, dancer, climber, player, painter, writer, baker, singer

Answers

Page 113
runner, jogger, drummer, swimmer, thinner, fatter

Page 114
"I have lost," she said sadly.
"They stole it!" we said angrily.
"We want more!" they said greedily.
"I want to go to bed," the toddler said sleepily.
"Woof! Woof!" the dog barked playfully.

Page 115
loudness, playfulness, cheapness, lateness, sickness, sadness, greatness, smoothness, clumsiness
The loudness of the thunder scared us all.
Kittens are known for their playfulness.
Some people get travel sickness.
She cried with happiness when she won.

Page 116
um/brell/a, snow/man, spi/der, mug, jell/y/fish, ward/robe, hol/i/day, oct/o/pus

Page 117
A/li, Mo/hamm/ad, Ell/a, Na/zeem, Is/a/bell/a, Ol/i/ver, Jim, Popp/y, Kat/ya, Ha/rry

Page 119
please, looked, called, asked, laughed, different, eyes, friends

Page 120
unwell, untidy, uneven, unfair, unhappy, unkind
Cinderella was unhappy because the stepsisters were unkind to her. She had to do all the housework. It was unfair. The stepsisters were very untidy.

Page 121
repay, remix, refill, refuel, rethink, rewind, rename, recall

Page 122
new, male, witch, place, threw

Page 123

b	p	l	a	c	e	s	s	v	s
n	l	d	d	w	h	e	r	e	o
m	a	i	l	m	a	l	e	e	w
a	i	d	t	w	e	r	e	t	w
i	c	t	h	r	o	u	g	h	r
n	e	h	e	t	a	i	l	r	w
m	t	e	i	c	z	z	n	e	i
a	d	r	r	d	k	n	e	w	t
n	w	e	a	r	s	e	w	b	c
e	t	a	l	e	w	h	i	c	h